D0540991

Published in Great Britain in MMXIII by
Book House, an imprint of
The Salariya Book Company Ltd
25 Marlborough Place, Brighton BN1 1UB
www.salariya.com
www.book-house.co.uk

PB ISBN-13: 978-1-908759-62-7

© The Salariya Book Company Ltd MMXIII

All rights reserved. No part of this publication may be reproduced, stored in or
introduced into a retrieval system or transmitted in any form, or by any means
(electronic, mechanical, photocopying, recording or otherwise) without the written permission of
the publisher. Any person who does any unauthorised act in relation to
this publication may be liable to criminal prosecution and civil claims for damages.

1 3 5 7 9 8 6 4 2

A CIP catalogue record for this book is available
from the British Library.
Printed and bound in China.
Printed on paper from sustainable sources.

This book is sold subject to the conditions that it shall not, by way of trade or
otherwise, be lent, resold, hired out, or otherwise circulated without the publisher's
prior consent in any form or binding or cover other than that in which it is published
and without similar condition being imposed on the subsequent purchaser.

Visit our website at **www.book-house.co.uk**
or go to **www.salariya.com**
for **free** electronic versions of:
You Wouldn't Want to be an Egyptian Mummy!
You Wouldn't Want to be a Roman Gladiator!
You Wouldn't Want to be a Polar Explorer!
You Wouldn't Want to Sail on a 19th-Century Whaling Ship!

Visit our **new** online shop at
shop.salariya.com
for great offers, gift ideas, all our new releases
and free postage and packaging.

KINGS & QUEENS

A VERY PECULIAR HISTORY

QUIZ BOOK

With added
blue blood

BRENT LIBRARIES

TOW

91120000105183

Askews & Holts	20-Mar-2013
J941.0099 JUNIOR NON	£5.99

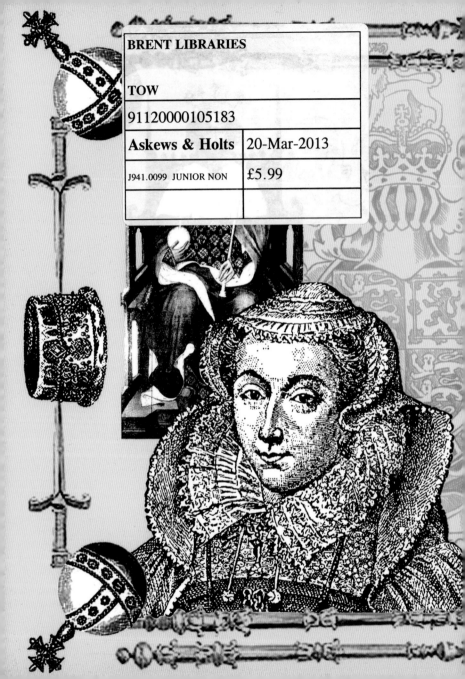

CONTENTS

INTRODUCTION

BRITAIN IS STILL RULED BY A QUEEN. WELL, 'RULED' MAY NOT BE QUITE THE RIGHT WORD, BUT SHE IS HEAD OF STATE, AND SHE STILL HAS A CONSIDERABLE AMOUNT OF INFLUENCE OVER THE WAY BRITAIN IS RUN. SOME 1,200 YEARS AGO KINGS HAD THE POWER TO DO JUST ABOUT ANYTHING THEY LIKED. THEY WERE NICE ONLY IF THEY WANTED TO BE, BUT GENERALLY GOT THEIR WAY THROUGH FORCE, GENERAL BULLYING, AND PERHAPS MURDER AND MAYHEM — IF NO-ONE MURDERED THEM FIRST.

THE ROLE OF A KING OR QUEEN IS DEEPLY EMBEDDED IN HISTORY, AND IS SURROUNDED BY AGE-OLD CEREMONY, RITUAL AND PAGEANT. THESE ARE IMPORTANT SYMBOLS OF BRITISH IDENTITY, AND POWERFUL STIMULANTS FOR FEELINGS OF NATIONAL PRIDE.

WITH THIS BOOK YOU CAN HAVE FUN WITH A WIDE SELECTION OF QUESTIONS AND ANSWERS ABOUT ALL THINGS ROYAL. CHALLENGE YOURSELF AND YOUR FRIENDS BY TESTING YOUR KNOWLEDGE OF THE BRITISH MONARCHY.

MEDIEVAL
MONARCHS

Q1

HOW MANY ASSASSINATION ATTEMPTS DID QUEEN VICTORIA SURVIVE?

a) 0
b) 3
c) 7
d) 12

Q2

WHICH OF THESE DID KING JAMES I (JAMES VI OF SCOTLAND) *NOT* WRITE A BOOK ON?

a) Witchcraft
b) The dangers of tobacco
c) The duties of kingship
d) Hunting

WHAT'S IN A NAME?

TODAY, ALMOST WITHOUT THINKING, WE CALL MONARCHS 'KING' OR 'QUEEN,' AND THE YOUNGER MEMBERS OF ROYAL FAMILIES 'PRINCE' OR 'PRINCESS'. TECHNICALLY, THIS IS NOT ALWAYS ACCURATE. FOR EXAMPLE, ZARA PHILLIPS HAS NO ROYAL TITLE, EVEN THOUGH QUEEN ELIZABETH II IS HER GRANDMOTHER.

IN THE PAST, TITLES OF RULING ROYALTY RANGED FROM MIGHTY EMPEROR TO LOWLY COUNT AND COUNTESS. THEIR CHILDREN MIGHT HAVE THE SAME TITLES, OR BE KNOWN SIMPLY AS 'LORD' AND 'LADY'. IN THIS BOOK WE HAVE – WE HOPE – CALLED PAST ROYAL PERSONS BY THEIR CORRECT TITLES. WE HAVE, HOWEVER, SOMETIMES USED THE GENERAL TERMS 'PRINCE' AND 'PRINCESS' WHEN REFERRING TO ROYALTY, OR FOR INDIVIDUALS TO AVOID CONFUSION.

Q3

WHAT IS THE NICKNAME OF RICHARD I?

a) The Lionheart
b) The Tigerheart
c) The Braveheart
d) The Strongheart

Q4

WHICH ONE OF THE FOLLOWING WAS *NOT* A SAXON KING?

a) Ethelwulf
b) Ethelward
c) Ethelbald
d) Ethelbert

ROYAL PICK AND MIX

IN 928, KING ÆTHELSTAN OF ENGLAND SENT TWO OF HIS DAUGHTERS ON A LONG JOURNEY ACROSS EUROPE TO THE COURT OF EMPEROR HENRY I. HIS PURPOSE? THE EMPEROR HAD AGREED TO CHOOSE ONE OF THEM AS A BRIDE FOR HIS SON OTTO, AND TO PASS THE 'REJECT' ON TO BE A WIFE FOR A LESS IMPORTANT PRINCE IN BURGUNDY.

Q5

WHO HAD BEEN CAUSING TROUBLE AROUND THE COASTS OF ENGLAND SINCE THE LATE 8TH CENTURY, SAILING IN THEIR LONGSHIPS FROM THEIR HOMELANDS IN NORWAY, SWEDEN AND DENMARK?

a) The Saxons
b) The Normans
c) The Vikings
d) The French

Q6

WHAT IS 'TANISTRY?'

a) A Scottish system of succession
b) Horseshoe-changing
c) Map-reading
d) A style of architecture

BRIDAL BONUS

IN 1469 A MARRIAGE WAS ARRANGED BETWEEN KING JAMES III OF SCOTLAND AND PRINCESS MARGARET OF DENMARK. THE WEDDING WENT AHEAD – BUT MARGARET'S FATHER COULD NOT AFFORD TO PAY HER AGREED DOWRY. SO KING JAMES SEIZED ORKNEY AND THE SHETLAND ISLES INSTEAD; FOR AROUND 600 YEARS THEY HAD BEEN RULED BY DENMARK, BUT NOW THEY BECAME PART OF SCOTLAND.

Q7

WHICH OF THE FOLLOWING GROUP OF PEOPLE DID
NOT SPEAK A FORM OF CELTIC?

a) Scots
b) Picts
c) Britons
d) Vikings

Q8

WHEN WAS THE BATTLE OF HASTINGS?

a) 562
b) 1066
c) 1246
d) 1468

Q9

WHAT IS THE NAME OF THE MASSIVE SURVEY OF ENGLAND CONDUCTED BY WILLIAM I, COUNTING WHO LIVED WHERE AND WHAT THEY OWNED?

a) The Tombsday Book
b) The Tuesday Book
c) The Domesday Book
d) William's Survey

Q10

WHAT TYPE OF ANIMALS ARE ON DUTY AT THE TOWER OF LONDON TODAY? ONE CAN BARK LIKE A DOG, WHILE ANOTHER SAYS 'HELLO' IN AN EERILY DEEP VOICE.

a) Parrots
b) Frogs
c) Ravens
d) Dogs

Q11

WHICH SHIP WAS WILLIAM OF MALMESBURY
WRITING ABOUT IN 1120 WHEN HE CLAIMED,
'NO SHIP EVER BROUGHT SO MUCH MISERY TO
ENGLAND?'

a) R.M.S *Titanic*
b) The *Mayflower*
c) The *Mary Rose*
d) The *White Ship*

Q12

IN 1154 NICHOLAS BREAKSPEAR BECAME THE ONLY
ENGLISH WHAT IN HISTORY?

a) Pope
b) Archbishop of Canterbury
c) Crusader
d) Saint

Q13

WHO LIVED WILD IN SHERWOOD FOREST, POACHING
DEER AND 'ROBBING THE RICH TO GIVE TO
THE POOR?'

a) Richard the Lionheart
b) Robin Hood and his band of Merry Men
c) The Sheriff of Nottingham
d) King John

HOW COMMON!

ONLY ONE OF QUEEN VICTORIA'S CHILDREN MARRIED A
MEMBER OF A NON-ROYAL FAMILY. AND SHE WED THE HEIR TO
A DUKEDOM — THE HIGHEST POSSIBLE RANK OF BRITISH
NOBILITY, JUST ONE DEGREE LOWER THAN ROYALTY. BY THE
LATE 19TH CENTURY, THAT WAS — JUST ABOUT — ACCEPTABLE.
BUT TRADITIONALLY, IF ROYALTY DARED TO WED ONE OF THEIR
LESS HIGH-RANKING SUBJECTS — KNOWN AS 'COMMONERS' —
THE MARRIAGE WAS EITHER CONDEMNED AS 'IMPOLITIC AND
UNPRECEDENTED' OR IT LED TO SCANDAL. IT MIGHT EVEN BE
AGAINST THE LAW.

Q14

WHAT IS 'CHIVALRY'?

a) A meat stew
b) A type of poetry
c) A code of honour
d) A knight's armour

Q15

WHERE DID KING JOHN SIGN THE MAGNA CARTA?

a) At the bottom of the page
b) At the top of the page
c) On the back of the page
d) He didn't sign it at all

I'M A LEGEND

HENRY VII BOASTED THAT HE WAS RELATED TO KING ARTHUR, AND NAMED HIS FIRST SON AFTER HIM. HE FIRST FELL IN LOVE WITH THE TALES OF THE KNIGHTS OF THE ROUND TABLE WHILE IN BRITTANY. IT'S NO COINCIDENCE THAT SIR THOMAS MALORY'S VERSION OF THE LEGEND, *LE MORTE D'ARTHUR*, WAS FIRST PRINTED BY WILLIAM CAXTON IN 1486, THE YEAR PRINCE ARTHUR WAS BAPTISED. IT WAS THE FIRST ROMANCE EVER PRINTED IN ENGLISH.

Q16

WHAT ANIMAL DID THE KING OF NORWAY GIVE TO HENRY III, FORMING THE BASIS OF A COLLECTION OF EXOTIC ANIMALS KEPT AT THE TOWER OF LONDON?

a) A polar bear
b) A sea lion
c) A penguin
d) A leopard

Q17

WHY WAS HENRY III'S ELDEST SON EDWARD GIVEN
THE NICKNAME 'LONGSHANKS'?

a) Because he had long hair
b) Because he had long legs
c) Because he had long fingers
d) Because he had a long nose

Q18

HOW OLD WAS ELEANOR OF CASTILE WHEN SHE
MARRIED EDWARD I?

a) 21
b) 45
c) 13
d) 32

Q19

IN 1348, WHAT ARRIVED ON THE SOUTH COAST AND
RAPIDLY SPREAD THROUGH THE COUNTRY?

a) Locusts
b) Grey squirrels
c) The plague
d) Tuberculosis

Q20

WHO LED THE PEASANTS' REVOLT IN 1381?

a) Wat Tyler
b) Henry Bolingbroke
c) The Archbishop of Canterbury
d) Oliver Cromwell

HUNGRY FOR A FIGHT

NAPOLEON ONCE SAID THAT 'AN ARMY MARCHES ON ITS STOMACH,' AND HENRY VIII WOULD HAVE HEARTILY AGREED. THE KING TOOK 200 KITCHEN STAFF WITH HIM TO FEED HIM WHILE ON CAMPAIGN, AND THE ROYAL KITCHENS WERE KEPT WELL STOCKED BY A TRAIN OF WAGONS WHICH INCLUDED:

- POULTRY WAGON
- MOBILE BAKERY
- WINE WAGON
- SWEET/CONFECTIONERY WAGON
- FRESH-FOOD LARDER.

IN CONTRAST, THE REST OF THE ENGLISH ARMY LIVED ON A SIMPLE DIET OF BEEF, BISCUITS AND BEER. OF THESE, BEER WAS BY FAR THE MOST IMPORTANT — EVEN AT COURT, MORE BEER WAS DRUNK THAN WINE. DURING A CAMPAIGN IN SPAIN IN 1512, HENRY'S THIRSTY ARMY REFUSED TO FIGHT WHEN THEY WERE OFFERED WINE OR CIDER INSTEAD OF BEER, AND THEIR COMMANDER WAS FORCED TO BRING THEM HOME!

Q21

HOW DID MARGARET THE 'MAID OF NORWAY' DIE?

a) She was beheaded.
b) She fell off her horse.
c) She was overcome by seasickness.
d) She caught the plague.

Q22

WHEN WAS THE BATTLE OF STIRLING BRIDGE?

a) 1154
b) 876
c) 1432
d) 1297

LIKE FATHER, LIKE SON

LIKE HIS FATHER, EDWARD VI WAS HORRIBLY SPOILT. NOTHING WAS TOO GRAND FOR THE FUTURE KING: ROOMS HUNG WITH EXPENSIVE TAPESTRIES, GOLD AND SILVER PLATES AND CUPS, CLOTHES AND BOOKS ENCRUSTED WITH PRECIOUS STONES AND GOLD. EVEN AS A YOUNG BOY, EDWARD OWNED MANY ANIMALS, INCLUDING A PACK OF HOUNDS AND FIGHTING BEARS, AND IN ONE (QUESTIONABLE) PORTRAIT, AGED 6, HE IS SHOWN HOLDING A MONKEY THAT MAY HAVE BELONGED TO THE COURT FOOL, WILL SOMERS.

Q23

FROM WHAT ANIMAL DID ROBERT THE BRUCE TAKE THE LESSON THAT WITH PATIENT PERSISTENCE, HE COULD SUCCEED IN DEFEATING THE ENGLISH?

a) A spider
b) A tortoise
c) A hare
d) A bull

TUDORS AND STUARTS

Q24

WHICH OF THE FOLLOWING IS CORRECT?

a) House of York: The Red Rose; House of Lancaster: The Yellow Rose
b) House of York: The White Rose; House of Lancaster: The Red Rose
c) House of York: The Yellow Rose; House of Lancaster: The White Rose
d) House of York: The White Rose; House of Lancaster: The Pink Rose

"
IN ANY COUNTRY, A KING MARRYING A SUBJECT IS LOOKED ON AS DISHONOURABLE.
"

BRITAIN'S KING GEORGE III, 1772
(HIS SON, THE FUTURE GEORGE IV, DID JUST THAT IN 1785.)

Q25

HOW MANY PRINCES WERE (PROBABLY) MURDERED IN THE TOWER OF LONDON IN 1483?

a) 2
b) 0
c) 1
d) 4

Q26

WHAT WAS THE NICKNAME OF QUEEN MARY I?

a) Scary Mary
b) Hairy Mary
c) Bloody Mary
d) Contrary Mary

Q27

THE WARS OF THE ROSES WERE BETWEEN WHICH TWO RIVAL FAMILIES?

a) Edward of York versus Henry VI from the House of Lancaster
b) Henry of York versus Henry VI from the House of Doncaster
c) Edward of York versus Henry III from the House of Lancaster
d) Edward III of York versus Richard III from the House of Lancaster

MY HUSBAND AND I

ARRANGED OR NOT, IN THE PAST THE AVERAGE ROYAL MARRIAGE DID NOT LAST VERY LONG. KINGS AND QUEENS EITHER DIED YOUNG, OR QUARRELLED AND SEPARATED. BRITAIN'S QUEEN ELIZABETH II IS THE FIRST RULING MONARCH TO CELEBRATE A DIAMOND WEDDING ANNIVERSARY. BY 2007, SHE AND HER HUSBAND, PRINCE PHILLIP, DUKE OF EDINBURGH, HAD BEEN MARRIED FOR 60 YEARS.

Q28

WHICH SPORT DID HENRY VII MAKE INTO A
FASHIONABLE GAME?

a) Real cricket
b) Real tennis
c) Boules
d) Real football

Q29

HENRY VIII WAS THE FIRST ENGLISH KING TO BE
CALLED WHAT?

a) Your Majesty
b) Your Royal Highness
c) The monarch
d) The sovereign

Q30

WHICH OF THE FOLLOWING DID HENRY VIII *NOT* ADD TO WHITEHALL PALACE BEFORE IT BURNED DOWN IN 1698?

a) Tennis courts
b) Bowling alley
c) A tiltyard for jousting
d) Ice-skating rink

Q31

WHICH ONE OF HENRY VIII'S WIVES WAS FIRST TO BE BEHEADED, IN 1536?

a) Jane Seymour
b) Anne Boleyn
c) Catherine Howard
d) Anne of Cleves

IN EVERY DETAIL

IN 1505, AFTER HIS WIFE HAD DIED, KING HENRY VII OF ENGLAND SENT AMBASSADORS TO SPAIN TO REPORT ON A POSSIBLE NEW BRIDE. PITY THE POOR ENVOYS! IT WAS THEIR TASK – WITHOUT CAUSING OFFENCE – TO PROVIDE ANSWERS TO 24 VERY DETAILED QUESTIONS ABOUT THE YOUNG LADY'S CHARACTER AND PHYSIQUE, SET BY THE KING. SOMEHOW, THEY HAD TO 'SEE HER HANDS BARE' (ROYALTY OFTEN WORE JEWELLED GLOVES) AND 'NOTE THE FASHION OF THEM...THICK OR LEAN...LONG OR SHORT'. ENCOURAGINGLY (OR PERHAPS JUST DIPLOMATICALLY), THE AMBASSADORS REPORTED THAT THE CANDIDATE'S HANDS WERE 'RIGHT FAIRE'.

Q32

WHICH THOMAS WAS ARRESTED AND DIED ON HIS WAY TO TRIAL?

a) More
b) Cromwell
c) Cranmer
d) Wolsey

Q33

REPORTEDLY, HOW MANY TIMES A MONTH DID
QUEEN ELIZABETH BATHE?

a) Once
b) Ten times
c) Twice
d) Never

Q34

HOW MANY BURNING SHIPS DID THE ENGLISH SEND
TOWARDS THE SPANISH ARMADA?

a) 0
b) 1
c) 8
d) 20

Q35

WHO WAS KNOWN AS THE 'VIRGIN QUEEN?'

a) Bloody Mary
b) Elizabeth I
c) Victoria
d) Elizabeth II

NO SAFETY IN NUMBERS

KING HENRY I (REIGNED 1154–1189) HOLDS THE RECORD AMONG ENGLISH KINGS FOR FATHERING THE LARGEST NUMBER OF CHILDREN. WITH HIS FIRST WIFE, QUEEN EDITH, HE HAD TWO SONS AND A DAUGHTER. HE ALSO HAD 20 (SOME SAY 24) ILLEGITIMATE CHILDREN WITH SEVERAL DIFFERENT MISTRESSES. YET HENRY LEFT NO MALE HEIR TO RULE AFTER HIM. BOTH HIS LAWFUL SONS DIED WHILE HE WAS STILL ALIVE; HIS UNLAWFUL SONS COULD NOT INHERIT HIS KINGDOM. AND WHEN HIS DAUGHTER, MATILDA, TRIED TO CLAIM HER FATHER'S KINGDOM, THERE WAS CIVIL WAR.

A ROYAL PROGRESS

ELIZABETH AND HER COURT TRAVELLED ACROSS SOUTHERN ENGLAND AND EAST ANGLIA ON SOME 25 'PROGRESSES' DURING HER REIGN. THESE YEARLY TOURS WERE A CHANCE FOR THE QUEEN TO BE SEEN IN PUBLIC, THOUGH THEY MUST HAVE BEEN A NIGHTMARE FOR HER SECURITY CHIEFS AS SHE STOPPED AND SPOKE TO ANYONE AND EVERYONE. SHE ALSO TUCKED IN TO LOCAL FOOD WITHOUT HAVING IT TASTED FIRST FOR SIGNS OF POISON.

A TYPICAL ROYAL PROGRESS TRAVELLED ABOUT 10 MILES (16 KM) A DAY. THERE WERE FEW GOOD ROADS, AND IN BAD WEATHER COACHES AND WAGONS SOON GOT STUCK IN THE MUD. THE QUEEN STAYED AT THE HOUSES OF NOBLES ALONG THE WAY. THOUGH THIS WAS A GREAT HONOUR, IT WAS ALSO A POTENTIAL MINEFIELD FOR THE HOST, WHO HAD TO INDULGE THE MONARCH WITHOUT APPEARING TOO FLASH. ELIZABETH EXPECTED THE FINEST ROOMS, LAVISH GIFTS OF JEWELLERY OR CLOTHES, AND A FULL LINE-UP OF ENTERTAINMENTS. WHEN SHE ARRIVED, EVERYTHING HAD TO BE JUST SO:

- FRESH PLASTER ON HOUSES
- FLAGS AND TAPESTRIES HANGING
- CLEAN TOILETS
- SWEPT CHIMNEYS
- NO ANIMALS IN STREETS
- THE ROYAL ROUTE STREWN WITH PETALS AND RUSHES.

Q36

WHY DID ELIZABETH I BRIEFLY IMPRISON SIR WALTER RALEIGH IN THE TOWER OF LONDON?

a) He secretly married one of her maids of honour.
b) He didn't throw his cloak down over a puddle.
c) He refused her proposal of marriage.
d) She didn't.

Q37

WHICH US STATE IS BELIEVED TO HAVE BEEN NAMED AFTER QUEEN ELIZABETH I?

a) North Carolina
b) Virginia
c) Florida
d) Maryland

ROYAL CHILDREN

DEVOTED COUPLE KING EDWARD I OF ENGLAND AND QUEEN ELEANOR OF CASTILE HAD 16 CHILDREN. OF THEIR 11 DAUGHTERS AND 5 SONS, 7 GIRLS AND ONE BOY (LATER EDWARD II) SURVIVED. WHEN ELEANOR DIED AGED 54, IN 1290, HENRY HAD 12 MEMORIAL CROSSES BUILT TO MARK THE PLACES WHERE HER COFFIN RESTED EACH NIGHT ON ITS LONG JOURNEY FROM NOTTINGHAMSHIRE TO THE ROYAL BURIAL PLACE AT WESTMINSTER ABBEY.

Q38

HOW OLD WAS MARY, QUEEN OF SCOTS, WHEN SHE WAS CROWNED QUEEN?

a) 9 months
b) 2 years
c) 13 years
d) 75 years

Q39

HOW DID ROBERT II OF SCOTLAND DIE IN 1390?

a) Plague
b) Grief
c) Old age
d) In battle

Q40

WHICH SCOTTISH KING WAS KILLED BY AN
EXPLODING CANNON IN 1460?

a) James I
b) James III
c) James V
d) James II

Q41

WHERE DID QUEEN ELIZABETH I KEEP MARY QUEEN
OF SCOTS CAPTIVE FOR 14 YEARS?

a) Tower of London
b) Sheffield Castle
c) Fotheringhay Castle
d) Stirling Castle

Q42

WHICH SPORT DID JAMES II TRY TO BAN BECAUSE IT
WAS SO POPULAR?

a) Football
b) Real tennis
c) Jousting
d) Golf

Q43

WHAT COLOUR IS THE BACKGROUND OF THE
SCOTTISH FLAG?

a) Red
b) Green
c) White
d) Blue

" A CAT MAY LOOK AT A KING. **"**

TRADITIONAL SAYING

Q44

WHICH KING SPONSORED AN ENGLISH TRANSLATION OF THE BIBLE?

a) James I
b) Charles I
c) James II
d) William III

Q45

HOW TALL WAS CHARLES I?

a) 1.7 m (5 ft 7 in)
b) 1.6 m (5 ft 4 in)
c) 1.9 m (6 ft 3 in)
d) 1.5 m (4 ft 11 in)

FOOD, GLORIOUS FOOD

THE ENGLISH WERE KNOWN AS GLUTTONS IN THE REST OF EUROPE, AND HENRY VIII SET THE EXAMPLE – ONE FEAST AT GREENWICH PALACE LASTED OVER 7 HOURS. THE 200-STRONG KITCHEN STAFF AT HAMPTON COURT PROVIDED MEALS OF UP TO 14 COURSES FOR SOME 600 PEOPLE IN THE GREAT HALL. MANY DISHES WERE DESIGNED TO SHOW OFF THE KING'S WEALTH AND POWER. SOME WERE JUST BIZARRE: A 'COCKATRICE' WAS MADE BY SEWING THE FRONT HALF OF A COCKEREL ONTO THE BACK HALF OF A BABY PIG! OTHER DISHES INCLUDED:

- SPIT-ROASTED BOAR   • GRILLED BEAVERS' TAILS
- WHALE MEAT   • WHOLE ROASTED PEACOCK
- TRIPE – LUNGS, SPLEEN AND EVEN COWS' UDDERS
- BOAR'S HEAD   • ROASTED SWAN   • MARZIPAN
- STRAWBERRIES AND CREAM.

THE DRINKS BILL AT HAMPTON COURT MUST HAVE BEEN ASTRONOMICAL: IN JUST ONE YEAR, HENRY AND HIS GUESTS QUAFFED 600,000 GALLONS (2.7 MILLION LITRES) OF ALE (MORE THAN ENOUGH TO FILL AN OLYMPIC-SIZE SWIMMING POOL) AND AROUND 75,000 GALLONS (341,000 LITRES) OF WINE (ENOUGH TO FILL 1,500 BATHTUBS).

HELLO, BIG BOY

ALL THAT EATING WAS BOUND TO AFFECT HENRY VIII'S WAISTLINE, AND AFTER A BAD JOUSTING INJURY IN 1536 THE LACK OF EXERCISE MADE THE KING EVEN FATTER. LATE PORTRAITS OF HENRY SHOW A MAN ALMOST AS WIDE AS HE WAS TALL — HIS WAIST MAY HAVE BEEN A BUTTON-BURSTING 60 IN (152 CM), COMPARED TO 35 IN (89 CM) AS A YOUNG MAN OF 23.

IN LATER LIFE THE KING NEEDED A STAFF TO HELP HIM WALK, AND BY 1545 HE WAS USING A WHEELCHAIR KNOWN AS A 'TRAMME', WHICH WAS PROBABLY PULLED ALONG BY MEN HEAVING ON ROPES. A FORM OF STAIRLIFT WAS BUILT TO HELP HIM CLIMB STAIRS AT WHITEHALL PALACE, WHILE ANOTHER DEVICE WINCHED HIM ONTO HIS HORSE.

TO HIDE HIS EXPANDING WAISTLINE, HENRY BEGAN WEARING PADDED CLOTHES WITH PUFFY SLEEVES. OUT OF RESPECT FOR THE KING, EVERYONE AT COURT STARTED WEARING PADDED CLOTHING TOO.

Q46

WHICH OF THE FOLLOWING DESCRIBES OLIVER CROMWELL'S ROUNDHEADS?

a) Fancy-clothed men wearing big feathered hats
b) A group of guard dogs
c) Puritans with shaven heads
d) Cromwell's music band

Q47

WHOSE HEAD IS BURIED IN SIDNEY SUSSEX COLLEGE, CAMBRIDGE?

a) Oliver Cromwell
b) Charles I
c) Charles II
d) Wat Tyler

Q48

WHERE DID THE GREAT FIRE OF LONDON START IN 1666?

a) Crumble Street
b) Pudding Lane
c) Porridge Road
d) Bakery Street

Q49

WHO WAS KNOWN AS THE 'MERRY MONARCH?'

a) Charles I
b) Richard I
c) Mary, Queen of Scots
d) Charles II

FROM MONARCH TO MONSTER

AS HE GREW OLDER, HENRY VIII BECAME MORE BEASTLY BY THE DAY:

• HE BEAT THOMAS CROMWELL AROUND THE HEAD AND SWORE AT HIM.

• WHEN HE GOT IN A STROP, HENRY CALLED HIS MINISTER THOMAS WRIOTHESLEY 'MY PIG'.

• AS AN OLD MAN, THE KING WOULD THREATEN HIS ENTIRE COURT BY SAYING 'THERE WAS NO HEAD SO FINE HE WOULD NOT MAKE IT FLY'.

• LOUIS PERREAU, FRENCH AMBASSADOR TO ENGLAND DURING THE 1530S, CALLED HIM 'THE MOST DANGEROUS AND CRUEL MAN IN THE WORLD'. PERREAU'S SUCCESSOR, CHARLES DE MARILLAC, SAID THAT HENRY 'DOES NOT TRUST A SINGLE MAN…AND HE WILL NOT CEASE TO DIP HIS HAND IN BLOOD AS LONG AS HE MISTRUSTS HIS PEOPLE'.

Q50

WHERE DID GEORGE II DIE?

a) In a brawl
b) At the Battle of Bosworth Field
c) On the toilet
d) In Berkeley Castle

"

I KNOW I HAVE THE BODY OF A WEAK AND FEEBLE WOMAN, BUT I HAVE THE HEART AND STOMACH OF A KING, AND OF A KING OF ENGLAND TOO.

"

ELIZABETH I TO HER ARMY AT TILBURY IN 1588

THE BRITISH NATIONAL ANTHEM

GOD SAVE OUR GRACIOUS QUEEN,
LONG LIVE OUR NOBLE QUEEN,
GOD SAVE THE QUEEN:
SEND HER VICTORIOUS,
HAPPY AND GLORIOUS,
LONG TO REIGN OVER US:
GOD SAVE THE QUEEN.

O LORD, OUR GOD, ARISE,
SCATTER HER ENEMIES,
AND MAKE THEM FALL.
CONFOUND THEIR POLITICS,
FRUSTRATE THEIR KNAVISH TRICKS,
ON THEE OUR HOPES WE FIX,
GOD SAVE US ALL.

THY CHOICEST GIFTS IN STORE,
ON HER BE PLEASED TO POUR;
LONG MAY SHE REIGN:
MAY SHE DEFEND OUR LAWS,
AND EVER GIVE US CAUSE
TO SING WITH HEART AND VOICE
'GOD SAVE THE QUEEN.'

Q51

WHICH OF THE FOLLOWING WAS A MEDICINE GIVEN TO CHARLES II WHEN HE WAS SUFFERING FROM MERCURY POISONING IN 1685?

a) Crushed human skull
b) Ground Egyptian mummy
c) Human blood
d) Nettle tea

Q52

WHAT WAS THE NAME OF THE PROTESTANT DUTCH PRINCE WHO WAS MARRIED TO MARY, DAUGHTER OF JAMES AND ANNE HYDE?

a) William of Orange
b) William of Yellow
c) William of Blue
d) William of Indigo

Q53

THE PERIOD BETWEEN 1688 AND 1694, WHERE WILLIAM III AND MARY II RULED JOINTLY AS EQUALS, WAS KNOWN AS WHAT?

a) Double Trouble
b) The Orange Revolution
c) The Double Revolution
d) The Glorious Revolution

'WE ARE NOT AMUSED'

THIS IS THE MOST FAMOUS QUOTATION ATTACHED TO QUEEN VICTORIA. BUT NO-ONE KNOWS QUITE WHEN SHE SAID IT, OR EVEN WHETHER SHE SAID IT ALL. IT SEEMS TO HAVE STUCK BECAUSE IT SOMEHOW SYMBOLISES THE SERIOUSNESS WITH WHICH VICTORIA UNDERTOOK HER DUTIES, AND HER GRIM DECADES OF UNSMILING MOURNING AFTER THE DEATH OF HER BELOVED PRINCE ALBERT.

Q54

HOW MANY CHILDREN DID QUEEN ANNE HAVE?

a) 0
b) 17
c) 4
d) 11

KENSINGTON PALACE

DESIGNED BY SIR CHRISTOPHER WREN FOR WILLIAM AND MARY, IT OPENED IN 1689 AT A TIME WHEN KENSINGTON WAS A VILLAGE OUTSIDE LONDON. IT WAS THE MAIN ROYAL RESIDENCE UNTIL THE DEATH OF GEORGE II IN 1760. MORE RECENTLY, IT HAS BEEN HOME TO PRINCESS MARGARET AND TO DIANA, PRINCESS OF WALES.

Q55

HOW MANY PEOPLE IS CHARLES II SAID TO HAVE
TOUCHED IN HIS LIFETIME?

a) 0
b) 15
c) 3,000
d) 92,000

Q56

WHO FLED 'OVER THE SEA TO SKYE' DISGUISED
AS A MAID?

a) The Prince Regent
b) Farmer George
c) Bonnie Prince Charlie
d) Soldier George

HANOVERIANS AND AFTER

Q57

DURING THE FRENCH REVOLUTION, WHAT FATE DID 16,000–40,000 PEOPLE SUFFER?

a) Executed by guillotine
b) Burned as witches
c) Imprisonment
d) Starvation

Q58

IN WHAT YEAR DID IRELAND JOIN THE UNION BETWEEN ENGLAND AND SCOTLAND, RESULTING IN THE UNION FLAG OR 'UNION JACK' DESIGN?

a) 1287
b) 1801
c) 1549
d) 1862

Q59

WHAT HAPPENED IN BOSTON THAT LED TO THE
DECLARATION OF INDEPENDENCE IN 1776?

a) Boston Tea Party
b) Boston Dinner Party
c) Boston Birthday Party
d) Boston Cocktail Party

THE LOST PRINCE

THE FIFTH CHILD OF GEORGE V, PRINCE JOHN (1905–1919),
SUFFERED FROM EPILEPSY. ALWAYS FRAGILE, HE WAS KEPT
OUT OF PUBLIC VIEW, AND LIVED MAINLY AT A FARM ON THE
SANDRINGHAM ESTATE IN NORFOLK, IN THE CARE OF A NANNY.
HE SUFFERED HIS FIRST EPILEPTIC SEIZURE WHEN HE WAS 4,
AND DID NOT ATTEND HIS FATHER'S CORONATION TWO YEARS
LATER. HE DIED AGED 13. IT IS A MEASURE OF THE NEED OF
THE ROYAL FAMILY TO MAINTAIN THE APPEARANCE OF
PERFECTION, THAT VERY LITTLE WAS KNOWN ABOUT HIM UNTIL
THE TV FILM *THE LOST PRINCE* WAS FIRST AIRED IN 2003.

Q60

WHAT WORD DID GEORGE III END ALL HIS SENTENCES WITH WHILE HE WAS SUFFERING FROM MENTAL ILLNESS?

a) Crown
b) Elephant
c) Mummy
d) Peacock

" TO BE A KING AND WEAR A CROWN IS A THING MORE GLORIOUS TO THEM THAT SEE IT THAN IT IS PLEASANT TO THEM THAT BEAR IT. "

QUEEN ELIZABETH I, 1601

EDWARD VIII AND MRS SIMPSON

AS PRINCE OF WALES, GEORGE V'S SON EDWARD (CALLED DAVID BY HIS FAMILY) WAS A POPULAR PUBLIC FIGURE — PARTYING WITH THE GLAMOROUS, FASHIONABLE LONDON SET, BUT SHOWING THAT HE HAD 'THE COMMON TOUCH' WHEN DEALING WITH ORDINARY WORKING PEOPLE.

BUT THERE WAS TROUBLE AHEAD. BY THE TIME HE BECAME KING, AS EDWARD VIII, IN 1936, HE WAS IN LOVE WITH AN AMERICAN WOMAN CALLED WALLIS SIMPSON — A DIVORCÉE SOON TO BE DIVORCED FOR THE SECOND TIME. PARLIAMENT DECLARED THAT MARRIAGE WAS IMPOSSIBLE: EITHER SHE WENT, OR EDWARD WOULD HAVE TO ABDICATE (GIVE UP THE THRONE). HE CHOSE LOVE AND DECIDED TO MARRY. SO EDWARD VIII REIGNED FOR UNDER A YEAR, BETWEEN JANUARY AND DECEMBER 1936, AND WAS NEVER CROWNED. HE BECAME THE FIRST AND ONLY ENGLISH MONARCH TO ABANDON THE THRONE VOLUNTARILY.

MANY PEOPLE IN BRITAIN WERE OUTRAGED; THEY THOUGHT A KING SHOULD SHOW A GREATER SENSE OF LOYALTY TO HIS PEOPLE, AND NOT PLACE HIS OWN SELFISH INTERESTS ABOVE HIS DUTY TO THE NATION. AFTER EDWARD VIII ABDICATED HE MARRIED WALLIS SIMPSON. THEY BECAME THE DUKE AND DUCHESS OF WINDSOR AND WENT TO LIVE ABROAD, MAINLY IN PARIS, WHERE HE DIED IN 1972.

Q61

WHAT TYPE OF POPULAR ART EMERGED DURING
GEORGIAN TIMES?

a) Collage
b) Pop art
c) Photographs
d) Cartoons

Q62

WHICH OF THE FOLLOWING IS AN EXOTIC STYLE NOT
FEATURED IN THE BRIGHTON PAVILION?

a) Moghul-Indian
b) Islamic
c) Chinese
d) German

Q63

WHO WAS LOCKED OUT OF THE PRINCE REGENT'S CORONATION CEREMONY AT WESTMINSTER ABBEY?

a) Maria Fitzherbert
b) The Prince Regent
c) Caroline of Brunswick
d) William IV

Q64

WHICH OF THE FOLLOWING WAS NOT PART OF THE PRINCE REGENT'S TYPICAL BREAKFAST?

a) Fruit salad
b) Laudanum (a poppy-based drug)
c) A beef pie
d) Champagne

Q65

HOW MANY CHILDREN DID WILLIAM IV AND HIS
MISTRESS, THE ACTRESS DOROTHEA BLAND, HAVE?

a) 0
b) 3
c) 5
d) 10

Q66

WHICH OF THE FOLLOWING WAS NOT A ROYAL
MISTRESS?

a) Bessie Bount
b) Lillie Langtry
c) Nell Gwyn
d) They all were.

Q67

WHAT WAS THE NAME OF QUEEN VICTORIA'S
HUSBAND?

a) Alexander
b) Albert
c) Augustus
d) Alfred

Q68

WHAT IS THE NAME OF THE PALACE BUILT FOR
QUEEN VICTORIA ON THE ISLE OF WIGHT?

a) Frogmore House
b) Kew Palace
c) Osborne House
d) Palace of Holyroodhouse

Q69

ROYAL WARRANTS WERE WITHDRAWN IN 1999 FOR SUPPLIERS OF WHAT?

a) Scotch whisky
b) Alcohol
c) Fine leather goods
d) Cigarettes

Q70

WHICH OF THE FOLLOWING WAS *NOT* ONE OF QUEEN VICTORIA'S NINE CHILDREN?

a) Prince George
b) Princess Victoria
c) Princess Louise
d) Prince Leopold

WHAT THE QUEEN DOES

'QUEEN ELIZABETH THE SECOND, BY THE GRACE OF GOD, OF GREAT BRITAIN AND NORTHERN IRELAND AND OF HER OTHER REALMS AND TERRITORIES, QUEEN, HEAD OF THE COMMONWEALTH, DEFENDER OF THE FAITH' – SO WENT HER JOB DESCRIPTION AT HER CORONATION IN 1953. BRITAIN HAS A CONSTITUTIONAL MONARCHY, WHICH IS TO SAY THAT THE KING OR QUEEN IS THE HEAD OF STATE, BUT HAS LIMITED POWER: RUNNING THE COUNTRY IS MAINLY CARRIED OUT BY THE GOVERNMENT AND PARLIAMENT.

THAT SAID, AFTER AN ELECTION IT IS THE QUEEN WHO INVITES THE LEADER OF THE LARGEST POLITICAL PARTY IN THE HOUSE OF COMMONS TO FORM A GOVERNMENT AND TO BECOME PRIME MINISTER. SHE ALSO FORMALLY DISSOLVES PARLIAMENT WHEN AN ELECTION IS REQUIRED. ALL ACTS OF PARLIAMENT HAVE TO RECEIVE THE ROYAL ASSENT BEFORE THEY BECOME LAW. THE PRIME MINISTER VISITS THE QUEEN ON A REGULAR BASIS TO DISCUSS POLITICAL AND NATIONAL MATTERS. IN HER CONSTITUTIONAL ROLE, THE QUEEN IS ASSISTED BY THE SELECTED GROUP OF SENIOR POLITICIANS WHO FORM HER PRIVY COUNCIL.

WILLY WILLY HARRY STEVE

A RHYME TO HELP YOU REMEMBER THE KINGS AND QUEENS OF ENGLAND:

WILLY, WILLY, HARRY, STEVE,
HENRY, DICK, JOHN, HENRY THREE;
THEN THREE EDWARDS, RICHARD TWO,
HENRY FOUR, FIVE, SIX, THEN WHO?
EDWARD FOUR, FIVE, DICK THE BAD,
TWO MORE HENRIES, NED THE LAD;
BLOODY MARY SHE CAME NEXT,
THEN WE HAVE OUR GOOD QUEEN BESS.
FROM SCOTLAND WE GOT JAMES THE VAIN;
CHARLIE ONE, TWO, JAMES AGAIN.
WILLIAM AND MARY, ANNA GLORIA,
FOUR GEORGES, WILLIAM AND VICTORIA.
EDWARD, GEORGE, THE SAME AGAIN,
NOW ELIZABETH — AND THE END.

THE ORDER OF SUCCESSION

SUCCESSION IN BRITAIN GOES THROUGH THE MALE LINE, IN THE FIRST INSTANCE — A SYSTEM CALLED 'MALE PRIMOGENITURE'. IF A MONARCH HAS SONS AND DAUGHTERS, THE SONS (AND THEIR OFFSPRING) TAKE PRECEDENCE. THE SONS OR DAUGHTERS OF THE MONARCH'S ELDEST SON TAKE PRECEDENCE OVER THE SECOND SON. A DAUGHTER WILL BECOME QUEEN ONLY IF SHE HAS NO LIVING BROTHERS, AND THERE ARE NO CHILDREN OF A BROTHER WHO HAS DIED.

1. CHARLES, PRINCE OF WALES
2. PRINCE WILLIAM OF WALES
3. PRINCE HENRY (HARRY) OF WALES
4. PRINCE ANDREW, DUKE OF YORK
5. PRINCESS BEATRICE OF YORK
6. PRINCESS EUGENIE OF YORK
7. PRINCE EDWARD, EARL OF WESSEX
8. JAMES, VISCOUNT SEVERN
9. LADY LOUISE WINDSOR
10. PRINCESS ANNE, THE PRINCESS ROYAL

ANSWERS

MEDIEVAL
MONARCHS

Q1: C. 7

Victoria is the longest-reigning British monarch and the longest-reigning queen regnant in world history; she reigned for a total of 63 years, 7 months and 2 days.

Q2: D. HUNTING

He also produced original poetry, as well as translations, a treatise on poetics, meditations and commentaries on the Scriptures, works of political theory and speeches to Parliament.

Q3: A. THE LIONHEART

He reigned from 1189 to 1199 and was the son of Henry II. Though born in Oxford, he spent little time in England.

Q4: B. ETHELWARD

Ethelwulf reigned from 839 to 858 and had five sons. Three of them, each called Ethel-something, ruled Wessex in quick succession.

Q5: C. THE VIKINGS

By the 9th century they had settled permanently in much of Britain, particularly in the North. The Viking royal families held power over kingdoms in Scandinavia as well as England.

Q6: A. A SCOTTISH SYSTEM OF SUCCESSION

The heir to the throne was chosen by election while the old king was still alive. The system lasted for nearly 200 years.

Q7: D. VIKINGS

After the Scots and the Picts united, Gaelic began to predominate, and Pictish faded away. The Angles spoke Anglo-Saxon, an early form of English.

Q8: B. 1066

After the Battle of Hastings, William, Duke of Normandy, became King of England, the first of the Norman kings.

Q9: C. THE DOMESDAY BOOK

The main purpose was to work out how much tax everyone should pay. All the details were recorded in a book, which became known as the Domesday Book, because paying taxes was like the Day of Doom.

Q10: C. RAVENS

It is said that if the ravens ever left the Tower, the monarchy would collapse.

Q11: D. THE *WHITE SHIP*

Sailing from France to England with many young members of the royal family, including the son and heir of Henry I, on board, the ship ran into rocks and capsized. The sole survivor was a French butcher.

Q12: A. POPE

He reached this position of great power and influence by rising through the ranks of the Church in France and Italy.

Q13: B. ROBIN HOOD AND HIS MERRY MEN

He is said to have been a nobleman whose lands were stolen by the cruel Sheriff of Nottingham. He may not have existed, but the legend is probably based on real-life characters.

Q14: C. A CODE OF HONOUR

Chivalry developed around the knights who fought in the Crusades – it denoted a mixture of courage, fighting skills, Christian devotion and loyalty.

Q15: D. HE DIDN'T SIGN IT AT ALL

Like most kings of his era, he could not read or write. Instead, he stamped the charter with the royal seal.

Q16: A. A POLAR BEAR

The polar bear was allowed to go fishing in the Thames!

Q17: B. HE HAD LONG LEGS

He was unusually tall, and as a warrior king he was determined to bring order throughout the land.

Q18: C. 13

When she died, Edward set up a series of 12 stone crosses to mark where her body had rested on its way to burial in Westminster Abbey; these included Charing Cross in London.

Q19: C. THE PLAGUE

Over the next two years or so, at least one third of the population of England died.

Q20: A. WAT TYLER

Thousands of peasants stormed to London, seized the Archbishop of Canterbury and other officials and chopped off their heads.

Q21: C. SEASICKNESS

Edward I of England proposed an arranged marriage between Margaret and his own son, but on her way to Scotland from Norway, aged 6, she died.

Q22: D. 1297

William Wallace's rag-tag army took on the English and won a resounding victory.

Q23: A. A SPIDER

He watched it busily trying to make its web: six times it failed before at last it succeeded.

TUDORS AND STUARTS

Q24: B. YORK: WHITE ROSE, LANCASTER: RED ROSE

There was a long-term rivalry between the House of Lancaster and the House of York, which was only resolved in 1485.

Q25: A. 2

The boy king Edward V, aged 12, and his younger brother Richard, Duke of York, aged 10, were locked up by their uncle, Richard, Duke of Gloucester.

Q26: C. BLOODY MARY

She was the daughter of Henry VIII and reigned from 1553 to 1558.

Q27: A. EDWARD OF YORK VERSUS HENRY VI

Both claimed the crown as descendants of Edward III. The result was a civil war that ran on and off for over 30 years.

Q28: B. REAL TENNIS

It was played in an indoor court, surrounded by walls, with a net in the middle. The modern game of lawn tennis was not invented until some 400 years later.

Q29: A. YOUR MAJESTY

This was somewhat typical of his inflated view of his own glory.

Q30: D. ICE-SKATING RINK

Built as the London residence of the Archbishop of York, the palace came into the hands of Cardinal Wolsey, who developed it as a fine residence; after his downfall in 1529, Henry VIII seized it.

Q31: B. ANNE BOLEYN

Anne was 15 years younger than Henry. Eight months after they were secretly married, they had a daughter, Elizabeth (later Queen Elizabeth I).

Q32: D. WOLSEY

Henry VIII gave him the job of persuading the Pope to permit his divorce from Catherine of Aragon, but he failed.

Q33: A. ONCE

The Elizabethans used perfumes to hide the smell of body odour, which mingled with the stench of chamber pots and sewers.

Q34: C. 8

When the Armada tried to flee from the flames, it was attacked off Gravelines and quickly routed.

Q35: B. ELIZABETH I

Elizabeth I courted a number of favourites, but she never did marry.

Q36: A. MARRIED ONE OF HER MAIDS OF HONOUR

On another occasion, Raleigh supposedly threw his cloak down in a puddle in front of Elizabeth, so that she wouldn't get her feet wet.

Q37: B. VIRGINIA

Maryland, USA is named after Henrietta Maria (wife of Charles I) and Georgia after George II.

Q38: A. 9 MONTHS

She was crowned at Stirling Castle as a baby of 9 months. Her mother, Mary of Guise, acted as regent, and brought her up as a Catholic.

Q39: C. OLD AGE

He had a fairly uneventful reign, during which he secured a succession by fathering 21 children.

Q40: D. JAMES II

He personally stabbed to death William, 8th Earl of Douglas in 1452. He was killed by a defective cannon at the siege of Roxburgh.

Q41: B. SHEFFIELD CASTLE

In 1586, letters written by Mary linked her to the Babington Plot to murder Elizabeth. She was tried for treason and beheaded at Fotheringhay Castle in 1587.

Q42: D. GOLF

This royal disapproval eventually evaporated, and a series of Scottish monarchs became avid enthusiasts.

Q43: D. BLUE

It is the cross of St Andrew, patron saint of Scotland, and is known to have been used for the flag of Scotland since the 1540s.

Q44: A. JAMES I

James I also commissioned the architect Inigo Jones to design two buildings in the newly fashionable Palladian classical style: the Banqueting Hall in Whitehall, and the Queen's House, Greenwich.

Q45: B. 1.6 M

He had very grand ideas about himself and married a witty and vivacious French princess, Henrietta Maria.

Q46: C. PURITANS WITH SHAVEN HEADS

They supported Parliament and fought against supporters of the King, who were nicknamed the Cavaliers.

Q47: A. OLIVER CROMWELL

He was originally buried in Westminster Abbey, but the year after the Restoration of the monarchy, fanatics tore up his grave and put his body through the process of execution.

Q48: B. PUDDING LANE

Official records suggest that very few people died, but much of London was destroyed.

Q49: D. CHARLES II

Charles had plenty of mistresses and numerous illegitimate children, but none by his wife, the Portuguese princess Catherine of Braganza.

Q50: C. ON THE TOILET

He died after eating en excessive amount of chocolate and suffering a heart attack.

Q51: A. CRUSHED HUMAN SKULL

He was taken ill on 2 February 1685 with violent fits. He was bled by physicians for four days.

Q52: A. WILLIAM OF ORANGE

William arrived in the little port of Brixham in Devon in 1688 and began his march on London.

Q53: D. THE GLORIOUS REVOLUTION

Mary died of smallpox in 1694, aged 32, after which William ruled alone.

Q54: B. 17

They all died in childhood. In her last years Anne became seriously ill, and so fat and lame she could barely leave Kensington Palace.

Q55: D. 92,000

People believed that kings and queens had divine powers and the ability to cure the sick through the 'Royal Touch'.

Q56: C. BONNIE PRINCE CHARLIE

In 1745 he launched a Jacobite rebellion from Scotland. He captured Edinburgh, won the Battle of Prestonpans and then headed south, getting to within 209 km (130 miles) of London before retreating.

HANOVERIANS AND AFTER

Q57: A. EXECUTED BY GUILLOTINE

In 1793 King Louis XVI and his queen Marie Antoinette were imprisoned and also executed by guillotine.

Q58: B. 1801

The flag is made up of the red cross of St George with the white X-shaped cross or saltire of St Andrew. The red saltire of St Patrick was added in 1801.

Q59: A. BOSTON TEA PARTY

In 1773, colonists in Boston rebelled against a tax on tea by throwing chests of tea from a ship into the harbour.

Q60: D. PEACOCK

This was probably caused by a disease of the blood called porphyria, which made him delusional.

Q61: D. CARTOONS

Cartoonists made prints poking fun at the excesses of politicians, doctors, generals, the nobility, the new industrial tycoons – and the royal family.

Q62: D. GERMAN

The Prince Regent's most extravagant project was his fantasy palace in Brighton, the newly fashionable seaside resort.

Q63: C. CAROLINE OF BRUNSWICK

In 1795, the Prince Regent was persuaded to marry his German cousin Caroline of Brunswick. He detested her, and they spent only two nights together – but this produced a daughter, Charlotte.

Q64: A. FRUIT SALAD

The Prince Regent was a glutton, and grew so fat he was nicknamed 'The Prince of Whales.'

Q65: D. 10

Illegitimate sons were often acknowledged by the name FitzRoy (*fils du roi*, 'son of the king').

Q66: D. THEY ALL WERE

Sophia von Kielmansegg was George I's mistress and was known as 'The Elephant' because she was short and fat.

Q67: B. ALBERT

Over time he adopted many public causes, such as educational reform and a worldwide abolition of slavery, and took on the responsibilities of running the Queen's household, estates and office.

Q68: C. OSBORNE HOUSE

It is now under the care of English Heritage and is open to the public, offering a unique insight into the family life of Queen Victoria.

Q69: D. CIGARETTES

Royal Warrants have been handed out to suppliers of goods and services to the royal family since the days of Henry II.

Q70: A. PRINCE GEORGE

Through her 9 children and 42 grandchildren, their marriages and family connections, Queen Victoria became the hub of a power network that spread across Europe.

A VERY PECULIAR HISTORY
QUIZ BOOKS

OTHER TITLES IN THIS SERIES:

EGYPTIAN MUMMIES
LONDON
BRIGHTON
CHRISTMAS
SCOTLAND

A VERY PECULIAR HISTORY

TITLES IN THIS SERIES:

WILLIAM SHAKESPEARE
SCOTTISH CLANS
SCOTTISH WORDS
SCOTTISH TARTAN
ROBERT BURNS
CHARLES DICKENS
THE 60s
FISHING
CRICKET
GOLF
WHISKY
THE OLYMPICS
WORLD WAR ONE
WORLD WAR TWO
QUEEN ELIZABETH II
VICTORIAN SERVANTS
YORKSHIRE

TITANIC
THE TUDORS
SCOTLAND VOLUME 1
SCOTLAND VOLUME 2
LONDON
CASTLES
IRELAND
BRIGHTON
CHRISTMAS
VAMPIRES
ANCIENT EGYPT
WALES
GLOBAL WARMING
RATIONS
THE BLITZ
KINGS AND QUEENS
GREAT BRITONS

www.salariya.com
where books come to life!